Name That Dog!

Puppy Poems From A to Z

Peggy Archer

illustrations by

Stephanie Buscema

SCHOLASTIC INC.

For Snickers, who inspired me, and for dog lovers everywhere—
especially the ones with dogs who "pop up" with the toast.
"Melody"—in memory of Mellie.
—P.A.

For Pamela and Brandon Buscema
—S.B.

No part of this publication may be reproduced, stored in a retrieval system, or transmitted in any form or by any means, electronic, mechanical, photocopying, recording, or otherwise, without written permission of the publisher. For information regarding permission, write to Dial Books for Young Readers, a division of Penguin Young Readers Group, a member of Penguin Group (USA) Inc., 345 Hudson Street, New York, NY 10014.

ISBN 978-0-545-60412-3

Text copyright © 2010 by Peggy Archer.
Illustrations copyright © 2010 by Stephanie Buscema. All rights reserved.
Published by Scholastic Inc., 557 Broadway, New York, NY 10012,
by arrangement with Dial Books for Young Readers, a division of Penguin
Young Readers Group, a member of Penguin Group (USA) Inc.
SCHOLASTIC and associated logos are trademarks and/or registered
trademarks of Scholastic Inc.

12 11 10 9 8 7 6 5 4 3 2 1   13 14 15 16 17 18/0

Printed in the U.S.A.   40

First Scholastic printing, April 2013

Designed by Jasmin Rubero
Text set in Pike

Name That Dog!

Happy puppies,
scrappy puppies,
    puppies playing games.
Shaggy puppies,
waggy puppies,
    each one needs a name.
A stick-fetching,
    ball-catching
      name that you can call
a yip-yapping,
    water-lapping
      puppy, big or small.
Perky puppies,
peppy puppies—
    none of them the same.
So jump into
    the alphabet and
      pick a puppy name!

Aspen

Yellow Labs like taxi cabs
and golden marmalade,
butterflies and fireflies
and homemade lemonade.
Yellow hay and sunshine rays
are things she likes to lay in.
And piles of leaves from aspen trees
are what she likes to play in.

Labrador Retriever

Bandit

My dog has two black patches
that cover up his eyes.
He sneaks around from room to room,
a bandit in disguise,

Stealing socks and slippers,
baseball caps and soap,
garden gloves and wooden spoons,
keys and jumping rope.

So if there's something missing,
like a book or cowboy boot,
just take a look by Bandit's bed—
that's where he keeps his loot.

Boston Terrier

Chewy

Chewing on the table leg.
Chewing on the chair.
Chewing on my running shoe.
Chewing on the stair.
Chewing on my baseball bat.
Chewing on the phone.
Chewing, chewing everything—
except her rawhide bone!

Field Spaniel

Daisy

She runs through Mother's petunias.
She thinks the pansies are fun.
Then she gets a bit lazy
and lies in the daisies
And quietly naps in the sun.

Dalmatian

Elvis

He wiggles and jiggles
and dances around.
He swings to the music
with a rock 'n' roll sound.
His ears look like sideburns.
His fur's long and black.
And sometimes I wonder
if Elvis is back!

Cocker Spaniel

Frank

He looks like a

Hot Dog

Wiener Dog

Frankfurter—

Frank.

Dachshund

Ghost

White towels and T-shirts
are usually quiet.
They sit there and don't move at all.
But sometimes they make quite
a ghostly appearance
on the head of a dog white and small.

Bedtimes are cozy,
all snuggled in blankets.
You peacefully dream in the night.
Except when you notice
a ghostly appearance
lying still on your bed, big and white.

If you have a white dog,
whatever the size,
Make sure that you're always aware—
if they like white T-shirts
or sleeping on blankets,
they sometimes can give you a scare!

West Highland
White Terrier (Westie)

Houdini

He wriggles from collars
and runs around free.
He unties the knots
from the rope on the tree.
He jumps over pet gates
in two seconds flat.
He digs under fences
with six-foot-high slats.
He unlatches latches
and slides open screens—
He's the greatest escape artist
I've ever seen!

Mini Pinscher

Indy

He likes
    wind-blowing
    ear-flapping
    rides in the car.
Anywhere.
Anytime.
    Near or far.

He's an
    Indiana race-dog—
    winner of the cup.
A speed-racer,
car-chaser,
    race-car pup.

Basset Fauve De Bretagne

Jingles

Tags for his house number.
Tags for his phone.
Shot tags.
Name tags
shaped like a bone.
Tags for his dog license,
one every year.
Jingle! Jangle!
Dog tags
tell you when he's near.

Bulldog

kingfisher

Just before dawn
when most are asleep
He quietly watches
in waters knee-deep.

He waits for the "big one."
He stakes out his prey.
Then swoops in and scoops in
the catch of the day.

Portuguese Water Dog

Liberty

Marching bands
Fire trucks
Flags held high.
Barbecues
Hot dogs
Ice cream, pie.
Firecrackers
Fireworks
up in the sky.
Little puppy
born on the
Fourth of July.

Rhodesian Ridgeback

Melody

She sings when I play the piano.
She croons to the saxophone blues.
She wails to that sad country music,
and moans to the nine o'clock news.

She boldly increases her volume,
enjoying the voice that she's found,
and sings a duet with the doorbell—
that howling, melodious hound.

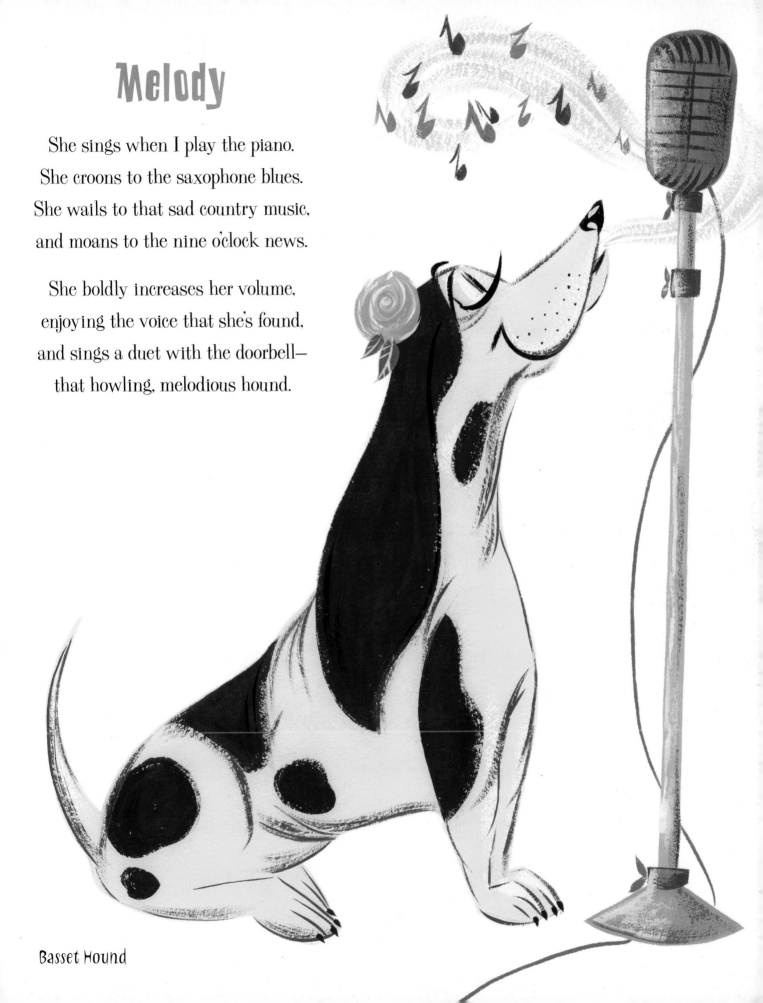

Basset Hound

Noodles

All over my puppy
are oodles and oodles
of swirls of fat curls that
remind me of noodles.

Poodle

Oscar

You sit when I tell you.
You fetch and you stay.
You stop and you come when I call.
You jump over boxes.
You give me your paw.
You run and you bring me the ball.

You pose for the camera
With puppy-dog eyes,
Then lie down and wait by my feet.
An Oscar performance—
A prize-winning show!
And all for a puppy-dog treat.

Niederlaufhund

Puddles

Sloshing through puddles
Splashing his toes
Leaving wet paw prints
Wherever he goes.

Drinking from puddles
Rain, cool and sweet.
Leaving more puddles
Behind on the street.

Scottish Terrier (Scottie)

Queenie

We bought her yummy doggy treats
for "sit," and "beg," and "stay."
She just sits there and looks at us
and gets them anyway.

She digs and barks and jumps and runs.
She doesn't listen, ever!
But Queenie knows she'll always rule
our house and hearts forever.

Lhasa Apso

Rex

My dog is just a puppy
But he's grown quite big so far.
He's bigger than his doghouse
And he won't fit in the car!

His teeth are big and pointy.
He has humongous feet.
His tongue is long and sloppy.
His tail can sweep the street.

Beef stew and juicy soup bones
Are foods he likes the best.
I have the perfect name for him—
Tyrannosaurus
REX.

Saint Bernard

Snickers

My dog's a creamy caramel
With chocolate ears and whiskers.
She's just a little nutty, too.
That's why I call her Snickers.

Mixed breed/mutt

Thor

(Norse god of thunder)

The forecast calls for sunshine.
There's not a cloud in sight.
But I have my own weather dog
whose instinct's always right.

He barks one time,
then starts to whine,
and scratches at the door,
long before the thunder starts—
my storm-predictor, Thor!

Doberman Pinscher

Ump

"Strike one!"   He barks!

"Strike two!"   Arf! Arf!

 Then, "Smack!" it's to the wall!

Sliiiide!   He howls!

"You're out!"   He growls—

    And runs off with the ball.

Beagle

Valentine

My friend gave me a puppy
with a card that said "Be Mine."
Now I'm head over heels
    the way puppy love feels
with that puppy—my Valentine.

Chihuahua

Whiskers

My dog has lots of whiskers
growing on his face.
Like a broom they sweep the floor
cleaning up the place.

You'll never find a scrap of food.
He does his very best.
He eats what he can find, and then
his whiskers catch the rest.

Schnauzer

Xerox

From the tops of his ears
to the tip of his tail
and everything else in between—
He couldn't have looked
any more like his dad
if he'd come from a copy machine!

Manchester Terriers

YOYO

He jumps up on the sofa.
He jumps down to the chair.
He bounces up to lick my face.
He races down the stair.

He jumps up by the window.
He jumps down to the floor.
He Loops the Loop, he Hops the Fence,
then comes back up for more.

He's a Roller Coaster falling.
He's a Rocket in the Sky.
He's up and down, he's Stop and Go,
like a yoyo whizzing by!

Boykin Spaniel

Zipper

Racing through the kitchen.
Running 'round the chair.
Chase the ball
down the hall.
Zipping everywhere!

Faster than a mustang.
Faster than a train.
Zip! he's here.
Zip! he's there.
Zipper is his name!

Dutch Smoushond

The Perfect Name

You can name some dogs for how they look
or what they like to eat.
You can name them for the way they act
when walking down the street.

You can name some dogs for flowers, or
for famous movie stars.
You can name them for the friends you like,
or for your favorite cars.

You can name them for their talents, or
their wiggy-waggy tails.
You can name them for the way they bark,
or go to fetch the mail.

With all the ways to name your dog,
when all is said and done,
whatever name you give your dog
will be the perfect one.